BELOW THE 45TH PARALLEL

The Beginner's Guide to Chasing the Aurora in the Great Lakes Region

Beat the odds.
Chase the Northern Lights in the mid-latitudes.
Make your dreams come true.

VOLUME I

By Melissa F. Kaelin
Founder of the Michigan Aurora Chasers

*Dedicated to every Aurora Chaser
who has helped me learn the art of the chase,
as well as those who have come along on the adventure,
especially Admin Nate Stovall and the Michigan Aurora Chasers.
Sincere gratitude also goes to our team of administrators, Gerry Beth
Buckel, Patrick Grubba, Marybeth Kiczenski, and Tim Wenzel.*

*Our communities thrive thanks to the inspiration,
mentorship and encouragement of people like you!*

Table of Contents

10 Years of Aurora Chasing

A deep peace in my soul.

That's what coursed through me when I leaned back onto the frosty grass on September 27, 2022, watching the Aurora dance overhead. The passion I have for the Northern Lights has changed my life in countless ways.

To celebrate ten years of chasing this rare natural phenomenon, I traveled to Alaska above the 65th Parallel — where I could dance with the Aurora in her own neighborhood. The North.

I met up with a team of eleven Aurora Chasers in Fairbanks, Alaska, to spend a week chasing the Northern Lights. With some of us starting out as strangers, we found a cozy house on a river with a north-facing view, and set to work plotting our route to clear skies, epic mountain views, and eventually, the Arctic Circle.

Only three days in, we were already slaying this challenge. We caught the Northern Lights three nights in a row. Sometimes, we only had to walk out on the back deck to glimpse a view. By the end of the week, we scored seven for eight on catching the Aurora and viewing the awesome colors with the human eye. Ironically, the only miss happened on a crystal clear, starry night when Auroral activity was all but nonexistent, with a Kp0. Outside of that, the Northern Lights consistently put on spectacular displays, stretching from horizon to horizon with breathtaking brightness, movement and color. That's Alaska!

I can't say I know everyone's story. I don't know what brought each of these wonderful members of our crew to love the Northern Lights, so much that they would travel to the northernmost parts of the world to view the Aurora's dance. But I do know my own story.

It's one of such deep change and transformation that I can hardly believe how far I've come since I caught my first Aurora in Taylors Falls, Minnesota on the night of October 1-2, 2013.

What's more, I can't believe how many amazing friends I have made, how many professional connections I have formed, how many scientific achievements I have witnessed, and how many natural mysteries have appeared right before my eyes.

Living this lifestyle is like wielding magic.

In the last decade, I have suffered unimaginable loss, experienced heartfelt healing, found courage I never knew I had, befriended humans across the globe, and come into my own. Now, I take pride in volunteering and leading an extraordinary community known as the Michigan Aurora Chasers, and working during the day as a professional science communicator with some of the foremost researchers on solar physics in the world.

For over 10 years, I chased subtle and brilliant Aurora Borealis both above and below the 45th Parallel. I witnessed vibrantly colorful pillars, lively dances across the sky, a faint corona overhead, and all-night displays on the coast of the Great Lakes. I caught Aurora in four different states, and once I even witnessed an Aurora so powerful, it was visible from just south of Minneapolis.

In 2022, I traveled to the top of the world to celebrate the amazing adventures I've shared with the community. I stayed in the pristine wilderness beneath the living skies. There, I experienced the moving nature of this ethereal phenomenon in all its glory. With our adventure crew, I reached the Arctic Circle and found out what it's like to experience the natural world at 66.33° North. Then, I kept going to catch the Aurora's dance above the 67th Parallel.

By our journey's end, I saw the Northern Lights illuminate the entire night sky with colors even I had never imagined, from neon green, violet and cranberry to a sunrise orange. I experienced the Aurora of a lifetime. The chase continues. And I am here for it! This adventure is an invigorating one, and it has uplifted my heart, mind, and soul.

No matter how many amazing displays I see, though, I love coming home. The most amazing feeling is catching the Aurora in your own backyard. That's how I began my time as an Aurora

Chaser, and that's what I want to pass on to you.

This guidebook is designed for the absolute beginner, in the hopes that the information here can help you view the Northern Lights for the first time.

The goal of this guide is to offer real advice and practical tips that you can use in the moment, when you are on the ground, to help you find the Aurora. The topics will help you understand the science on a surface level, show you what it takes to successfully chase Aurora, and give you pointers that may keep you safe and satisfied along the way.

Together, I hope we can make your dreams come true! I can't think of a better way to celebrate my passion for chasing the light.

— *Melissa F. Kaelin*
Writer, Artist & Stargazer
Founder of the Michigan Aurora Chasers
December 15, 2022

Guidebook Cover Photo
The cover photo was taken by Melissa F. Kaelin during her trip to Alaska, in the Arctic Circle on September 29, 2022. The photo was taken using only an iPhone 14 on a tripod, demonstrating the advances in phone technology and low light photography.

Embarking on the Chase: Commonly Used Terms

When people first start chasing the Northern Lights, they are often surprised to learn several things.

First, it's much harder than it looks. Second, the Aurora you see may be much more subtle than what you've seen in popular media. Third, if you truly want to be successful, there is a huge learning curve — including a daunting number of terms and definitions that describe the natural phenomenon we know as the Northern Lights.

To experienced Aurora Chasers, the adventure becomes its own art form. There are many methods of Aurora forecasting, and none of them are necessarily wrong, if they help you catch the Aurora. There are also many types of Aurora, many approaches to Aurora photography, and many terms you need to know to be successful.

With absolute beginners in mind, here are a few fun ones to help you get started.

The 45th Parallel — a celebrated latitude line located halfway between the Equator and the North Pole, where the Aurora Borealis enters Earth's atmosphere. Aurora sightings are much more common above the 45th Parallel, making this northern area a magical place! With dedication, it is possible to catch Aurora below the 45th Parallel.

Aurora — a luminous phenomenon displaying patterns of light in the upper atmosphere of a planet's magnetic polar regions, including the North Pole (Aurora Borealis) and the South Pole (Aurora Australis). Not all auroral activity is created equal, and there are many variations and related sights to see in the night sky, such as proton arcs, STEVE and the picket fence.

Geomagnetic Activity — activity related to the magnetic properties of our planet, when there is an exchange of energy from the solar wind into the environment surrounding Earth, creating Aurora.

Solar Wind — the flow of charged particles released from the upper atmosphere of the sun that travels through the solar system.

Kp Index (K/Kp) — an index of aurora strength measured on a scale of 0 to 9, with 9 being the highest. When denoted as Kp, this indicates a "planetary" average of K measured at locations around the world over the last 3-hour time period.

Bz — the gatekeeper of the Aurora; Bz is a component of the Interplanetary Magnetic Field that indicates whether the polarity is tipped northward (positive) to protect Earth's atmosphere from solar wind, or southward (negative) to let solar wind flow into the atmosphere and create Aurora.

Ovation Model — the OVATION (Oval Variation, Assessment, Tracking, Intensity, and Online Nowcasting) model is an empirical model of the intensity of the Aurora operated by the NOAA Space Weather Prediction Center. The model uses the solar wind velocity and Interplanetary Magnetic Field measures at the L1 point located about 1 million miles upstream from Earth to estimate the probability of Aurora viewing.

Space Weather — conditions in the region of space close to Earth, especially the presence of charged particles and electromagnetic waves emitted by the sun, that can affect human activity and technology. Aurora is created as a result of space weather.

Unpredictable — Some things in life are nearly impossible to predict! Trying to predict the Aurora, or the weather in space, is like trying to predict the weather on Earth, only a thousand times harder. Not only does our weather have to align with space weather, but this is also an emerging science. New spacecraft, research, forecasting models and theories are introduced all the time, and yet, we still have much to learn. If you have trouble catching the Aurora, dust off and try again. It can take a lot of patience, strength and persistence to be successful in this pursuit.

RESOURCE > *Find a comprehensive glossary of terms online thanks to the experts at the NOAA Space Weather Prediction Center. For the link and details, visit: KaelinArt.com/45thParallel*

Train Your Eyes on the Sky: A Field Guide

Have you ever chased the Northern Lights in the U.S.? You may have been looking right at the Aurora and not even realized it!

How is this possible? Well, not every Aurora is vivid and colorful and flowing with movement. Sometimes, Northern Lights are just the opposite. Sometimes, they are subtle and quick. Sometimes, they don't look like much more than clouds.

Not every Aurora takes the same formation either, to mirror the displays you see in the movies and pop culture. The Northern Lights take on many different formations. They can appear in the shape of an arc, a valley of dunes, enormous pillars, or a glorious corona seemingly drifting down from the center of the sky.

Not to mention, STEVE. This sub-auroral arc with an interesting acronym appears more southward in the sky. It's unmistakable with a bright stripe and it often appears with a pronounced "picket fence." STEVE stands for the Strong Thermal Enhancement Velocity Emission. STEVE is also different than the routine and beautiful vertical pillars that appear during strong Aurora displays.

Unfortunately, many first-time Aurora Chasers are fooled by large patches of light pollution. They see the colors above a city in the sky and mistake the yellow-orange light created by artificial bulbs for Aurora. This stale glow hangs above population centers and other concentrations of artificial light, filling the darkness with its constant presence.

So, how do you know when you've found the Northern Lights? The good news is there a few sure signs of Aurora, even for those who are trying to catch a rare appearance at lower latitudes, where Northern Lights just aren't as bright.

Embrace the darkness

A lot of first-time chasers make the mistake of stealing one quick look at the sky, and then declaring the adventure a success or a failure. If you can spot the Aurora that easily in the mid-latitudes, fantastic! It must be a vibrant show!

Usually, it takes a bit more work.

Here's what you need to do:

- **Go outside.** This may seem obvious, and we all fantasize about watching the Northern Lights from our bedroom window, a sunroof, or a glass igloo in Finland. It is possible! But let's be honest, it helps if you go outside. Sometimes, even the pane of a window or a soft glow from the other room can be enough to reduce your viewing experience. Chances are, your eyes are going to acclimate better to the night sky if you go outside, even in your own backyard.

- **Take a test shot on your camera or phone.** Now, as someone who prefers to see the Aurora with my own eyes, I usually skip this step. However, our human eyes were not designed to see well at night. The fact of the matter is that a camera picks up more light and color in the dark than the rods and cones in our eyes. So, you may detect Northern Lights first on your camera preview screen, before you can actually see them with the unaided eye. A view through the camera lens can serve as a preview of better things to come. Be advised, your test shot may not be accurate if your camera settings are wrong or your phone camera is too weak for night photography. Still, even a blurry photo could give you a sense of what's out there.

- **Turn off your devices or put them away.** The brightness of your car headlights, the red and green indicators on your dashboard, the glow of your cell phone, the white beam of your flashlight: All of these light sources can muddle your viewing experience. If you stay in your car with the dash lights on, you could be sitting under an Aurora display and not even know it, because it's not strong enough to detect from inside the car. Sometimes, it will be. Often, it won't. Make your surroundings as dark as you possibly can.

- **Let your eyes adjust to the dark.** Once you get out into the darkness, it's time to embrace it. Take a break from checking your devices, turn off your flashlight, and gaze into the sky. A lot of people recommend you let your eyes adjust for 30-60 seconds. Better yet, let your eyes adjust to the dark for five full minutes. During this time, you will start seeing better in the dark. You will start noticing more. The ground beneath you will seem easier to navigate. Not only will you catch a few shooting stars, but you may also start to see light you didn't realize was there before.

- **Focus your attention low on the northern horizon.** As a naked-eye Aurora Chaser, I can't emphasize this enough. I usually start a night of Aurora Chasing by staring intently at the northern end of one of the Great Lakes, letting my eyes acclimate to the darkness and observing the sky for any changes in color, shape or movement. If an Aurora display is just beginning, it will begin in the shape of a subtle arc across the northern sky, stretching from east to west. If the Aurora has already gained power, it will extend outward and upward from this arc. When the display is in full swing, you're sure to see the formations and movement on the northern horizon and to quickly notice the Northern Lights expanding much higher into the sky, sometimes extending directly overhead!

- **Be patient and give it time.** By nature, humans are not nocturnal creatures. So, you may feel tempted to step outside, take a quick look, dismiss any possibility of Aurora, and go back to bed. But good Aurora displays take time to build, especially at our latitude. The Northern Lights may flicker or flirt with the sky for a moment or two, disappear, reappear, disappear for longer, and then finally gain enough power to burst into full color and put on a show. Don't let those 5 or 10 minute lulls fool you. If you're truly chasing and hoping to catch Aurora, I would recommend devoting at least 2-3 hours to the chase. That way, you have a chance to appreciate the night, to learn the changes in the dark skies, to catch a shooting star, and to see Northern Lights, even if the Aurora is coming in waves. Of course, the most successful Aurora Chasers will devote an entire night to observing the sky.

- **Don't ruin your night vision.** Now that you are immersed in the darkness, enjoying all the night sky has to offer, don't waste your eyes on artificial light. Personally, I'm terrible at this. As a curious person and someone who monitors the data, I'm always tempted to look up the newest stats and active conditions on my phone. But each time I do that, my eyes lose their focus, and seeing in the dark becomes difficult again. If a colorful Aurora were to leap into the sky at just that moment, I would miss it! Because I would still be retraining my eyes to the dark.

- **Know the signs of Aurora.** This may come as a surprise to people who rarely go out at night, but there are actually a lot of light sources in the dark. Sunset sometimes has a lasting effect on the sky. Twilight brings a beautiful gradient of orange, green and blue. Clouds can shine in the moonlight. Light pollution is everywhere we look. And other human-made light sources appear from time to time, such as theatrical spotlights, the glow of a greenhouse, boat lights or party lights.

RESOURCE > *Learn more about some variations in the types of Aurora. Find interesting articles based in scientific discovery. To read more, visit: KaelinArt.com/45thParallel*

Aurora Chasing
Below the 45th Parallel

When our 35,000 Michigan Aurora Chasers got discouraged after months of quiet skies, I took a closer look at the odds. What are the odds of capturing a vivid Northern Lights display below the 45th Parallel? What are the chances of catching an Aurora sighting as far south as the 42nd Parallel? Better yet, how often can you realistically catch Aurora in Michigan or the Great Lakes region without the aid of a camera?

This curiosity led me to jot down a quick guide for those who are new to the chase. These tips might be especially helpful to those who have tried over and over again to see Northern Lights, but returned home with no luck.

If you're a beginner chasing the Aurora Borealis at lower latitudes, maybe this will help you find the lights!

TL ; DR
Most people who chase below the 45th Parallel are more likely to see Aurora with a K6/G2 Storm or higher. Yes, Aurora Chasing advice can absolutely help you catch the Northern Lights! But no, it won't be easy at lower latitudes.

Know what it takes in the mid-latitudes

The year of 2022 marked my fourth year living in Michigan. Because scientists first thought we hit solar minimum in December 2019, which was shortly after my move to Michigan from Minnesota, it has taken me a while to get a feel for local Aurora conditions. Now, I understand our latitude better and what it takes to see Aurora below the 45th Parallel.

When I chase Aurora, I like to see it with my own eyes, and I don't bring a camera. Naturally, this leads me to wait for stronger shows, when the probability of Northern Lights is extremely high. That's right, sometimes Aurora is only visible with the help of a camera. Sometimes, the Aurora is just too subtle or far away for us to actually see it in the sky.

That said, I think the best conditions for sighting visible Aurora in Michigan in general could be a G2 Storm, equivalent to K6, or higher. That kind of geomagnetic storm would reach all corners of Michigan — even Ohio. Note that in the first months after the Michigan Aurora Chasers was founded, we had not seen anything above K5, or a minor geomagnetic storm, in the forecast. We knew we would see more powerful geomagnetic storms predicted at some point, but G2 Storms and G3 Storms are very rare.

K-index	Aurora Strength	Storm Level Description
K-0	—	
K-1	—	
K-2	—	
K-3	—	
K-4	—	
K-5	G1 Storm	Minor Geomagnetic Storm
K-6	G2 Storm	Moderate Geomagnetic Storm
K-7	G3 Storm	Strong Geomagnetic Storm
K-8	G4 Storm	Severe Geomagnetic Storm
K-9	G5 Storm	Extreme Geomagnetic Storm

(Source: NOAA Space Weather Prediction Center)

In Michigan, much of the state's population is below the 45th Parallel, with the Michigan-Ohio border roughly marking the 42nd Parallel. Aurora are more common the farther north you go, which makes it difficult for anyone along the 42nd Parallel (Grand Rapids 42.9°, Lansing 42.7°, Detroit 42.3°, Ann Arbor 42.2°, Toledo 41.6°) to catch Northern Lights.

Surrounded by the gorgeous Great Lakes, Michigan residents also have to contend with a fair amount of lake effect weather, which complicates the scene for sky watchers. In fact, Michigan ranks in the 10 cloudiest states in the U.S., according to Farmer's Almanac.

The best conditions for sightings in the Great Lakes region vary quite a bit, because we have so many latitudes represented in this area of the Midwest. Different areas of the region also have different levels of light pollution to consider, especially where cities and population centers thrive.

Keeping our focus on the Great Lakes region, the northernmost point of Lake Superior on the U.S. side takes us slightly north of the 48th Parallel, with Pigeon River, Minnesota sitting at 48.01° N. The southernmost point of the Great Lakes takes us slightly southwest of Mitiwanga, Ohio sitting at 41.38° N. Seven degrees of latitude makes a significant difference when it comes to Aurora Chasing, because even moving one degree north can increase your chances of a sighting. In northern Minnesota, it's not uncommon to catch visible Aurora at a strength of K3, and it's very likely at a strength of K4. In locations that are closer to the 42nd Parallel, like Ohio, Indiana or Illinois, it would likely take a strength of K6, or better yet K7, to view the Northern Lights. New York is another variable, because of the state's many latitudes, but a K6 should be strong enough to bring subtle Aurora to most of the state. Of course, Canada has all the fun!

That's why there's so much interest in Aurora Chasing groups in the mid-latitudes, right? We want to help each other spot Aurora on the RARE occasions it dips this far south when we have clear skies for good viewing.

Now, you might be able to see Aurora at many power levels and values on the K-index in the Great Lakes region, especially in Michigan's Upper Peninsula, northern Wisconsin, Minnesota or any location above the 45th Parallel — where this advice is irrelevant! But to view the Northern Lights below the 45th Parallel, with an aurora strength of K3, K4, or K5, or even higher, you really need to know your stuff.

RESOURCE > *Understand your latitude. Get tips for determining what parallel is closest to your home or the place where you hope to see Northern Lights. See how latitude plays out on a map of the Great Lakes region. For details, visit: KaelinArt.com/45thParallel*

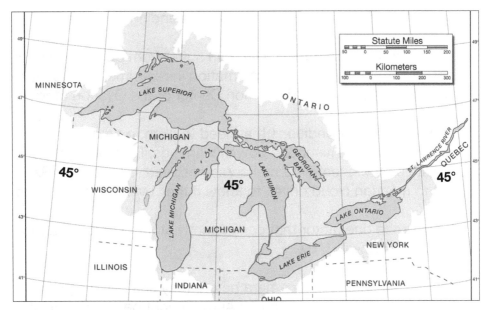

Source: NOAA Great Lakes Environmental Research Laboratory

Tips to catch the Northern Lights

Astrophotographers who take stunning photos in the mid-latitudes do all of these things:

- Scout out their own beautiful locations for viewing during the daylight, so they know the terrain and don't fall through the ice while shooting in the dark

- Use dark sky maps or light pollution maps to determine what nearby location has the best dark sky viewing with no major cities or light pollution directly to the north

- Make plans to experience other amazing sights on their journey, so they are not disappointed if and when an Aurora forecast doesn't pan out

- Check forecasts for earth weather (clouds, fog and wildfire smoke) and space weather to understand how likely it is that Northern Lights will appear, and double-check conditions right before heading out in case something changes

- Use apps, satellite data, and live sightings to check Aurora strength and to monitor how Aurora is trending over time

- Go beyond mobile apps, which can suffer from delays or lag, to consult original sources of information in real-time, such as the NOAA Space Weather Prediction Center or the Ovation Model

- Learn the many conditions that need to align to create visible Aurora: Using hemispheric power, warnings, latitude, light pollution maps, real-time measures of speed, density and Bz, not to mention cloud cover, to know if they even have a chance

- Monitor the one factor that can instantly stop a show if it turns positive/northward: Bz

- Take a test shot with a camera before they see anything with the naked eye, to understand if Aurora might be present at all

-

- Stand outside all night long so they don't miss a minute, with backup plans to safely take a nap, chew hard candies or drink caffeinated beverages to stay awake

- Respect public park guidelines and avoid loitering on private property (Gun owners may carry when they come outside to investigate unexpected activity on their property in the dark)

- Work together to stay informed or call for help when an emergency arises

- Master their camera settings to capture vivid light

Yes! Those who have knowledge and experience absolutely can help you catch the Northern Lights! But no, it won't be easy in the mid-latitudes.

Those who are successful at our latitude will be those who either:
a) Learn as much as they can and keep trying no matter how discouraging it gets, or
b) Wait until a real-time sighting is posted online and get lucky by being in the right place at the right time to catch a view.

A Simple Guide to Forecasting Aurora in the U.S.

Once you get a sense of what it's like to chase the Northern Lights in the mid-latitudes, you may find you need more information to make a sighting happen! That may leave you wanting an in-depth explanation of the Aurora forecasts. So, let's break it down.

What causes the Northern Lights and why is it so difficult to predict? In simple terms, our planet's Aurora are created by the solar wind that is emitted from the sun's surface. A solar flare (or other activity on the sun) sends solar plasma speeding into space, and scientists work to predict the resulting impacts on our atmosphere.

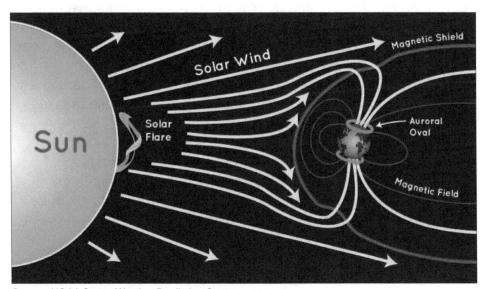

Source: NOAA Space Weather Prediction Center

If the solar wind penetrates Earth's atmosphere, it interacts with air molecules to emit light — creating the Northern Lights!

Why doesn't it always work out?

- Sometimes, the solar wind blows right past our planet, and what could have been a hit becomes a miss.

- Sometimes, the solar wind flows effortlessly into the atmosphere, helped by magnetic field conditions. (This happens when we have **negative/southward Bz**. Bz is a component of the Interplanetary Magnetic Field that, in simple terms, determines whether or not Earth's atmosphere is open to the solar wind.)
- Sometimes, the solar wind moves slower or faster than anticipated, making the forecast irrelevant, pushing the predicted conditions one day earlier or one day later, and causing us to miss the display.
- Sometimes, the solar wind makes a direct hit, but Earth's magnetic field flips like a polarized magnet and blocks any solar matter from entering the atmosphere. (This happens when we have sustained positive/northward Bz.) In this case, any predicted activity usually becomes a dud in the mid-latitudes.

For a good Northern Lights display in the mid-latitudes, we need solar wind that is fast (high speed), substantial (high density), able to enter our atmosphere (low Bz), and packs a lot of power (power can be measured by gigawatts of hemispheric power, or by the K-index). In the Great Lakes region, we also need clear, dark skies for good viewing conditions, which can be rare because of lake effect weather.

The strongest Aurora events reach what we call "storm levels," causing geomagnetic storms ranked at G1 (same as Kp5), G2 (Kp6), G3 (Kp7), G4 (Kp8) or G5 (same as Kp9 — which might be able to wipe out the planet's electrical grid!)

Unless you are very experienced and know what to look for, you are probably not going to see Northern Lights above the 45th parallel until it reaches at least Kp4 on the K-index (a scale of 0-9). At Kp4, the northernmost parts of the continental U.S. might get lucky. More likely, we need a G1 Storm (Kp5) to provide good viewing for anyone above the 45th parallel. Below the 45th parallel, you would typically need a G2 Storm (Kp6) or stronger to view Northern Lights. Other factors considered, a G2 Storm should be strong enough to send Aurora dancing anywhere in the U.S. and Canada that rests above the 42nd parallel.

Keep in mind, apps and other websites often give you the "Kp," with the "p" making the stat a "planetary average" of what has happened over the last 3 hours and not necessarily an indication of future conditions. That said, many maps are available that show you what K or Kp you would need to view Aurora at your latitude. This value will always remain the same. It's just a question of whether the Northern Lights on any given night will achieve that kind of power, and that high of a K/Kp value, radiating southward from the North Pole, where Aurora Borealis enters our atmosphere. (Aurora Australis also radiates northward from the South Pole.)

Regardless, when speed, density, Bz and other factors cooperate, the Aurora can surprise us. Those who are truly devoted to staying up all night to monitor the skies can capture Aurora for short intervals pretty frequently in the northern U.S. states — when the conditions align. Obviously, Alaska enjoys even better displays.

The science behind aurora forecasts

It's a science!

Auroral activity is monitored in order to protect our infrastructure and resources on Earth from risky side effects, such as impacts on GPS, electrical surges, and drag on satellites that orbit the Earth. So, in some cases, the forecasts could be designed to over-predict potential activity, to help government agencies manage the potential risks. The forecasts are always given in Universal Coordinated Time (UTC), which is a scientific standard.

The best data we have appears in real time. The short-term forecasts, which often predict Aurora strength that is greater than the actual activity, come from NOAA's Space Weather Prediction Center. These forecasts are given 2-3 days in advance, which is about how much time it takes solar plasma to travel from the sun's surface to Earth's atmosphere.

My advice? Use the forecasts more as a guide for when to be alert, not as an exact schedule. Know what K/Kp you need to view the Northern Lights at your latitude. Find a mapped visual or real-time resource that works for you. Use social media to help you on your chase. Watch for real-time alerts, changes in the data, and live sightings, if you want reliable info. Find the darkest skies near you using a light pollution or dark sky map. Before you go out, check local forecasts for cloud cover and clear skies.

Most of all, make plans that will lead you to enjoy the night, no matter what the conditions bring!

We call it "Aurora Chasing," not "Aurora Viewing," for a reason. That's because the Aurora is so extremely difficult to predict, even for the most experienced scientists. A huge part of this passion is enjoying the chase!

RESOURCE > *If questions arise or you want to watch live Aurora sightings roll in, you can join one of many area groups devoted to Aurora Chasing. For suggestions, visit: KaelinArt.com/45thParallel*

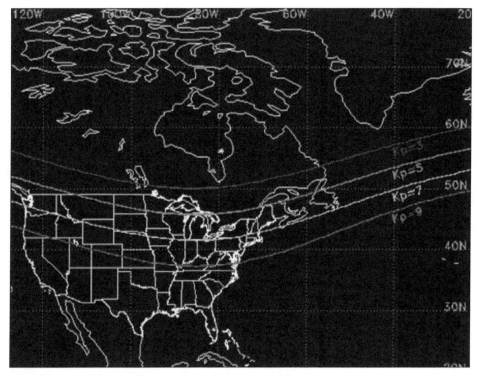

(Image by NOAA Space Weather Prediction Center.)

The Pros and Cons of Relying on Kp

When you're trying to catch the Northern Lights for the first time, it's natural to wonder when you can see them and where. The answer to these questions, it turns out, is not so easy. Even our best indicators in Aurora forecasting come with strengths and weaknesses.

Enter the K-index.

In simple terms, the K-index is a measure of Aurora strength on a scale of 0 to 9, with K9 being the highest possible strength. When given as Kp, this denotes a planetary average of the K value over a span of three hours, after it is measured at magnetometers around the world. Aurora activity can be much more localized, which is part of the reason chasing Aurora can be so difficult, varied, and specific to a certain region. Use a Kp map *(left)* to help guide you.

The K/Kp values also correspond to geomagnetic storm conditions. When the K-index reaches a value of 5, for example, it is synonymous with a minor geomagnetic storm, also known as a G1 Storm. For Aurora viewers, storm conditions are a good thing.

Be careful how you use the K-index. Seasoned Aurora Chasers know that this indicator works best when compared with other types of information to gauge the true possibility of Northern Lights. In fact, many Aurora groups and amateur forecasters avoid using the K-index altogether, because they don't view the predicted Kp as a solid indication that Northern Lights will appear. The K-index can be a useful tool for forecasting the Aurora, but it doesn't work as well in real time.

So, what is a solid indicator? That's a more advanced question, because many conditions have to align in order for us to see the Northern Lights. A good discussion might involve the Bz, Bt, Speed, Density, and Hemispheric Power, or a real-time forecasting model, at the very least.

Let's stick to Kp for now.

An Aurora Chaser's guide to understanding Kp

Keep in mind, there are many ways Kp can help you on the chase. The trick is to learn the meanings, know what to look for in your region, and take K-index measures with a grain of salt.

It's the gold standard. The K-index is the standard used in forecasts by the NOAA Space Weather Prediction Center and other government agencies. It's what the agency uses to alert subscribers using both their 3-day forecasts and the 27-day outlook, which makes it a valuable prediction tool.

It always refers to the same places on the map. The way K/Kp forecasts are depicted, the values correspond to a location on the map, designated by latitude. This relationship stays the same. So, if you learn that you typically need a Kp4 to view Aurora at your latitude, you will always look for Kp4 or stronger.

It's a forecasting tool. Also known as space weather, Aurora is a difficult phenomenon to predict. Forecasting space weather is not unlike forecasting the weather here on Earth. Potential impacts can move in a different direction and conditions can change quickly, rendering some of the advice from forecasters irrelevant.

I would recommend reading such forecasts the same way you might read an iffy Earth weather forecast — hope for the best, but be prepared for the worst. We never know which way the space weather will turn!

It's data gathered from magnetometers across the globe. To calculate the K-index, scientists use measurements of Aurora strength from magnetometers around the world, like those in Boulder, Colorado, or Kiruna, Sweden. They generate the K value on an index that's based on fluctuations in the geomagnetic field detected in near real-time. Geomagnetic activity is synonymous with Aurora activity, so understanding this is key!

It's an average. When referred to as the Kp, the K-index gives a planetary "p" average of geomagnetic activity, and it indicates the average of the activity that occurred over a span of three hours.

It sometimes refers to the past. Aurora forecasts and Kp alerts are distributed based on activity that happens in three-hour increments of Universal Coordinated Time. That means when you check the Kp, you could very well be seeing the average Aurora strength from three hours in the *past*. While Kp is useful for understanding the trends of the Aurora on any given night, it does not necessarily indicate future activity.

It may change. A space weather forecast is just that: a forecast. Conditions may change unexpectedly, not unlike the way weather in our atmosphere often takes unexpected turns for the better or worse. The NOAA Space Weather Prediction Center issues many Watches for potential activity, but they also issue stronger Warnings for conditions they are able to detect. Let me draw an analogy. When we look at the difference between a Tornado Watch and a Tornado Warning, we can see that these indicators are very different. A Watch is issued when the conditions are right to create a tornado, however, a Warning is issued when a tornado has been spotted on the ground. While Watches let us know when to be alert, a Warning suggests that a storm is emminent. That said, a forecast of K/Kp can change at any time. As scientists make space weather forecasts more accessible to the public, you can receive these alerts, watches and warnings right in your email inbox with a subscription to NOAA's forecasting service.

It's often an over-prediction. The reason Aurora forecasts exist is to protect systems and infrastructure from powerful pulses and impacts coming from outside the Earth's atmosphere. Strong impacts can cause drag on satellites, power grid fluctuations, false alarm triggering, and transformer damage, to name a few. At least during the last 10 years or so, the agencies that predict this type of activity have tried to warn against the strongest possible conditions at any given time. For us, that means a 3-day forecast could be exaggerated, and we could see much lower activity than what was initially predicted. As the models used in space weather forecasting and the teams at the helm change, there is potential for the approach to forecasting to change as well.

It's available on many apps, which might delay or lag. One of the reasons Kp is so popular is because it is widely distributed on many apps, with the option to have your phone or mobile device send alerts when Kp reaches a certain level. A potential pitfall is that apps need to be maintained and updated too, and they are drawing information from other sources before relaying that information to you. So, there may be delays or a lag in receiving this information. That's why I often recommend getting your information from a direct source, like the NOAA Space Weather Prediction Center. It never hurts to go straight to the website of an original source to take a look at the raw data. Personally, I find that this approach leads me to be much more successful on the chase.

It's not an exact science. Just like a weather forecaster might not be able to tell you that it is going to start raining exactly at 11:03 p.m. Eastern, it's difficult for forecasters to pinpoint the exact time that Aurora may appear. The NOAA Space Weather Prediction Center issues their most reliable Aurora forecasts only 2-3 days in advance of a potential display.

The timing of these forecasts is given in three-hour increments of Universal Coordinated Time, but that doesn't mean the Northern Lights will begin appearing at exactly 03:00 UTC. On a good day, it could! More than likely, though, the timestamps will mark a window of time when active conditions begin to build, and windows of time when the Aurora become extremely active.

That's why I recommend using forecast times more like a guide for when to be alert, not a schedule.

It's arguably the wrong data to consider in real-time. While the K/Kp can be useful in Aurora forecasting, the best data comes in real-time. As darkness approaches, it's often best to turn your attention to other indicators and look at other types of data. How much speed are we getting? How much density is it packing? Is the Bz (a component of the Interplanetary Magnetic Field) cooperating so that we can witness an Aurora display?

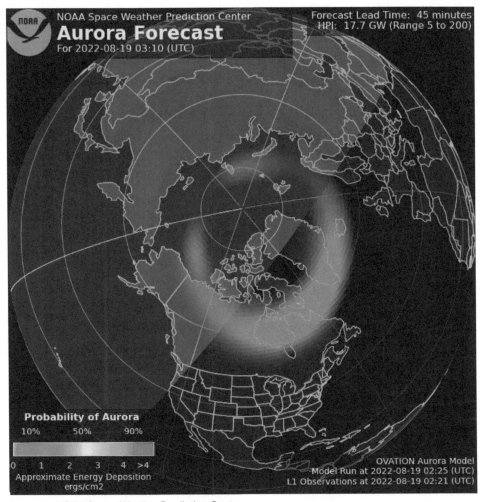

Image by NOAA Space Weather Prediction Center.

It's not the only indicator of active conditions. There are many different methods and sources that can be used to gauge Aurora activity, and Kp is just one of them. In fact, when other conditions align, such as a high speed and density of the solar wind combined with a negative/southward Bz, you might catch Aurora right in your backyard — even with a low Kp.

In a decade of Aurora Chasing, I have witnessed many times just like this. The forecasts and reported Kp came in very low, say Kp2, yet devoted photographers captured the Northern Lights in the mid-latitudes. You just never know!

As you chase the Northern Lights, consider other forecasts and factors, like the hemispheric power index (HPI.) Displayed on the Ovation Model, the hemispheric power index gives a different measure of the aurora's power. Learn what strength the HPI needs to reach for the Aurora to appear at your latitude.

Experienced Aurora Chasers may be able to spot Aurora above the 45th Parallel with a hemispheric power of 30 gigawatts, even if it is only camera-visible. A measure of 60gw makes a visible display above the 45th Parallel much more likely and gives photographers below the 45th Parallel hope. For Aurora Chasers below the 45th Parallel to have a solid chance of an Aurora sighting with the naked eye, we need the hemispheric power to climb well over 60gw, better yet 90-100gw.

RESOURCE > *Find out how to subscribe for email or text updates directly from the source, the government forecasting agency. The 3-day forecasts from the NOAA Space Weather Forecast Center are issued in Universal Time, and there is also an easy-to-use website available for time conversions in the U.S. For a step-by-step guide to this subscription service, visit: KaelinArt.com/45thParallel*

Sure Fire Signs of Aurora

So, what are some of the signs that give Aurora away, and guarantee you're not admiring light pollution in the dark?

Aurora creates formations. Whether you see the arc low on the horizon, stretching from east to west, or spot pillars or columns of light reaching up into the sky, the Northern Lights will take on interesting shapes and formations that are rarely seen elsewhere.

Aurora moves, flows and dances. It moves! This is one of the major differences between Northern Lights and light pollution. While light pollution or even cloud cover can hold the same position for long periods of time, the Northern Lights will almost always show some movement. Aurora might expand and reach higher into the sky during a short amount of time, flow through the night like a veil or curtains, or flit across the sky in a fast-moving choreography. Watch for the movement.

Aurora changes, gradually or rapidly depending on the display. Northern Lights expand and brighten as they take on more strength, and they fade away when a geomagnetic storm loses power. Sometimes, a display of Aurora will be so fast-moving that you can jolt your head around, trying to catch all the commotion and activity as lights and colors dart across the heavens. Even if there are only slight differences over time, the Aurora will change as you watch it.

Aurora flickers, pulses and shimmers. During extremely strong activity, the Aurora may bring more than light, form and color to the show. It can flicker, pulse with light, or shimmer in the sky.

Aurora drapes over the sky like a translucent veil. Usually, you can look through an Aurora and see the stars behind it. If you can't see the stars, you may not be looking at the Northern Lights. That's because air molecules are interacting with solar matter to emit light and color at different altitudes. The light is being created throughout the sky, but it is not opaque like a cloud. This light is translucent, and it appears like the air itself has transformed into a different color.

Aurora takes on stunning natural colors. Forget stale oranges, muddy yellows or siren blues. Especially with the help of a camera, the Aurora will display phenomenal natural colors that are beautiful to see. Unfortunately, in the mid-latitudes, the colors are only visible to the unaided eye during very strong conditions or geomagnetic storms. So, at first, the Aurora may appear to be white or silver. But when you see those vibrant colors pop, you'll know without a doubt that you've caught the Northern Lights!

When in doubt, check the map. If you feel uncertain that you're seeing Aurora, make sure that the way you were looking or taking photos at the time was facing north. Double check to ensure no major cities were located to your north, even up to 30 or 60 miles away. Light pollution can be seen from great distances. Drive by odd light sources to get a closer look and identify if there is an attraction or facility nearby that's obscuring your view. Or set a goal to travel to darker, more northern skies.

Many people say after they catch the Aurora for the first time, they know what to look for. All it takes is one great chase to kick-start a lifetime of Aurora Chasing!

RESOURCE > *Tap into some of the easiest and most reliable Aurora forecasting tools available on the internet. Many of these tools offer intuitive visualizations that show you where Aurora may be visible on the map. For a list of my favorite forecasting tools and links to find them, visit: KaelinArt.com/45thParallel*

Delight Your Eyes: How to View Aurora with the Unaided Eye in the Lower 48 States

A little known fact about Aurora Chasing in the U.S.: During weak to average displays, you often can't see the Northern Lights with the naked eye. That's right. Too often, you can't even see the Aurora!

What?! How can you chase something you can't see?

Well, it takes some creativity. The creativity of using a camera, in fact. As you now realize, our human eyes are not designed to help us see well at night. The rods and cones in our eyes cannot detect the full spectrum of light in the dark. But a camera does!

At lower latitudes, Northern Lights often show up on a DSLR camera, before they appear to the naked eye. As the Aurora gains strength, it may then become visible without the use of a camera. Or it may hide from view, drifting just below the stars and comets until sunrise.

Even if Aurora is visible to the eye, it often appears without color, instead forming white pillars or silver veils above the northern horizon. This could be why so many first-time Aurora Chasers have trouble spotting the Northern Lights.

Aurora doesn't always look like the colorful designs shown in photos, videos and popular culture.

This is especially true for the lower latitudes. Chase at a latitude anywhere south of the 45th Parallel, and you're looking for a beacon of light that's glowing from the distant, far north.
So much farther north, that it may linger like an invisible friend — not much more than an idea floating out on the horizon.

So, how do you see it? Train your eyes to the sky using this field guide, or give it time and wait patiently to see if the Northern Lights will brighten up their dance.

When can I witness color with my own eyes?

Experienced Aurora Chasers in the lower 48 states agree: Sadly, we can't predict visible color in the Northern Lights at these latitudes. Especially not as low as the 42nd Parallel, where an eager community of Michigan Aurora Chasers inspired this advice.

If you'd like to see color with your own eyes, your best bet is to watch for live sightings and eye-witness accounts on social media, indicating that people are actually seeing vivid lights in the area where you live. Then get outside fast!

There are simply too many variables to predict naked-eye color, the first being your own eyesight. Because our eyes don't see well in the dark, a camera will always pick up more color, even without any photo editing at all. In fact, Aurora photographers must sometimes tone down their photos in post processing, to make their photos appear as subtle as the vision appeared in real life.

Each person also has their own unique individual eyesight. No one can know how well your eyes will perform in the dark using night vision, except for you — and maybe your eye doctor. Experiences will differ based on a broad range of factors, spanning from the use of corrective lenses, age, and colorblindness, to other physical and genetic factors.

Even if we could know when the average person will see colorful Aurora in the dark at lower latitudes, there are too many factors involved in the composition of the Aurora to make this predictable.

Many Aurora Chasers believe that a high density or an extremely low Bz can lead to more visible color. In addition, those factors can be influenced by solar wind speed, Bt, a positive polarity of the solar plasma, or how much the magnetosphere engaged with previous solar wind activity.

So, if you want to truly understand when to see visible color in the mid-latitudes, you will need to build your understanding of the science of space weather. Another alternative is to learn by doing, as you gain more real-world experience viewing the Northern Lights. Often, we learn just as much from our failures as we do from our successes.

Delight your eyes: Tips to improve the odds

No matter how challenging it is, I'll share some advice that could help you catch a gorgeous Aurora display at lower latitudes with your own eyes.

And for most people, it is very challenging below the 45th Parallel.

So, how can you increase your chances of catching visible color in the Northern Lights? Well, there is no tried-and-true formula, but there are some things you can do to improve your aurora viewing experience.

- Generally speaking, the most powerful numbers in Aurora data allow us to see Northern Lights more vividly. Learn what these values are by reading websites and watching the trends of different Aurora displays. Wait for powerful geomagnetic storms, such as G1 Storms, G2 Storms, G3 Storms, or higher. (At least, a Kp5.)
- In addition to storm conditions, look for high solar wind speed, high Bt, and especially high density. You're going to need every data point working in your favor to produce the best results.
- Chase Aurora when Bz, a component of the Interplanetary Magnetic Field, is at its lowest values. Fondly known as the gatekeeper, that pesky Bz should be tipped as far negative or southward as possible with sustained numbers in that direction. I look for Bz values of -10 or -15 when I am hoping to catch a naked-eye visible display.
- Find the darkest skies possible using a dark sky map, which can be found online easily with a quick search.
- Avoid Aurora chasing with centers of light pollution to the north of your location.
- Go as far north as possible, to increase your chances of

viewing a fantastic display and seeing the colors.

- Plan to stay out all night so that you don't miss the peak of an Aurora display, which often appears in the pre-dawn hours.
- Chase when there are no obstructions, such as a bright full moon, fog, or wildfire smoke.
- Use the phases of the moon to your advantage. The Aurora will be most visible to the eye in the mid-latitudes during a new moon or periods of extremely low moonlight. Get out before the moon rises or stay out after the moon sets, because the sky will be darker then.
- Try chasing under clear, winter skies for less precipitation or more clarity in the crisp, cold air.
- Take a camera so you can detect what colors are possible and you can see when the Aurora are getting stronger, even if naked-eye visibility doesn't pan out. If the colors appear on camera and brighten with time, this is a good sign. The Aurora may soon appear in its full glory to the unaided eye.

You might even want to consider taking a trip north of the U.S. during the colder months, when naked-eye visible colors are a common occurrence for people living closer to the North Pole.

If your heart is in it, I truly hope you get to experience the wonder of a colorful Aurora display one day! Nothing can match this awe-inspiring experience.

RESOURCE > *Aurora forecasting apps can be misleading, because they try to oversimplify information about the potential for Northern Lights. Aurora is nuanced and unpredictable. Find out what apps experienced Aurora Chasers recommend, and download an app that helps you learn as you go. For recommendations, visit: KaelinArt.com/45thParallel*

An Ideal Perspective: Scout Out the Best Viewing Locations

Over 10 years of Aurora Chasing, I've come to appreciate the difference between being below the 45th parallel, which doesn't really feel like the north to me, and above the 45th parallel, which is much better for Aurora Chasing in my experience.

On a fun side note, North Dakota is one of the few U.S. states that rests entirely above the 45th parallel!

It's possible to view the Northern Lights below the 45th Parallel, of course. But this can take a lot of dedication, extremely strong space weather conditions, and an ideal viewing location.

Giving out tips on the best viewing locations can be a controversial issue in Aurora Chasing groups. Just think about other hobbyists such as geocachers, mushroom foragers, rock collectors, hunters or fishers. When they reveal their most treasured spots, they may have to compete for space along a river or lakeshore. Or they may not be able to find their treasures because everyone else got their first.

Now, there's plenty of Aurora to go around! That's the good news.

Just like anything in nature, though, the best viewing locations can be vulnerable to human exposure. Therein lies the bad news. Whether a location provides a home for protected wildlife, becomes susceptible to erosion or decay, or risks getting dangerously overcrowded, there are many issues to consider when venturing into nature at night.

I'd like to thank everyone who has helped share tips on locations for new Aurora Chasers. You're very generous with your advice, and those of us who run Aurora Chasing groups appreciate your help. As you share these tips, please keep in mind that sometimes large hobby groups result in high traffic or overcrowding at these locations, and it is not always sustainable in the local environment.

Feel free to keep your best and most primitive viewing spots a secret, and be mindful of whether a location can support a large group of viewers when you share it here. That's my advice, at least!

Personally, I am not against sharing viewing locations. But I do sometimes feel anxious or concerned when a mass gathering occurs in a previously unknown location. Will the gathering go smoothly? Will anyone get lost or injured? Will there be enough parking? Will a problem arise for law enforcement?

That's why I think this information should be given out carefully and kept off of public forums. When you see someone looking for a viewing location, why not share that information privately, one on one? Another good option is to only share tips on locations in small groups. This can prevent a number of issues, before they start.

Maybe I sound a bit stand-offish when it comes to the question of "Where" to view Aurora, but it truly is a question that can — and should — be answered on your own. If you're new at this, here are a few tips that can help you scout of the best viewing locations.

I believe the best viewing location is one that you have:
a) Traveled to in both daylight and darkness to evaluate safety and darkness. Don't fall in a lake in the dark because you didn't know it was there!
b) Found within a close or reasonable drive to your home or current lodging
c) Scouted out on your own to avoid unsustainable crowding
d) Checked laws and regulations to ensure you can stay there safely, and
e) Chosen with your own creative vision in mind to achieve unique foregrounds and silhouettes in your photos.

If you do receive a tip on viewing locations, please remember to be respectful of the land and the inhabitants (wild or human) when you go. That's my two cents!

What's the bottom line? Anywhere with clear, dark skies and a northward facing view will work. At Kp6 (which is very rare, granted) Northern Lights may be visible anywhere in Michigan, and in many states in the northern tier of the U.S. So, just find dark skies!

Dark sky parks: A good place to start

We're fortunate in the lower 48 states to have many beautiful parks and publicly owned lands for recreational use. While it is quickly becoming a dwindling resource, we're also lucky to have many parks devoted to preserving the dark sky.

Dark Sky Parks make a perfect destination for Aurora Chasers. They are located far from light pollution centers, they often include amenities that keep human needs in mind, and they are usually open for long periods of darkness — or even 24 hours a day. When you visit these parks, even if you don't catch the Northern Lights, you'll be able to view shooting stars, comets, the Milky Way, and the International Space Station as it makes its routine pass in orbit.

Better yet, International Dark Sky Parks offer even more perks for stargazers and night sky enthusiasts. These parks must demonstrate that they hold a number of qualities that lead to better dark sky viewing, natural preservation and a better future for our planet and our communities.

Aurora Chasing on the open road

Do you ever take road trips? Do you ever watch for opportunities to stop alongside the road and take in the scenery?

Have you ever paused for a moment to watch the sunset or view the Milky Way? Or the northern horizon? One of the best places to do this is at roadside parks! I love that we have so many in the Midwest, especially along the Great Lakes shoreline. Some of the most magical views I've seen have been sunsets on these routes.

Next time you're looking for a viewing location, why not stop at a roadside park if Aurora are active? These areas tend to be safe, well-marked spots with enough parking for passers-by. Some will even have small peninsulas or sections that are very dark, tucked away from the traffic. To find one, just search your mobile maps or the internet for "Roadside Parks!"

This general guideline is one I'm happy to share regarding Aurora viewing locations. I believe everyone should scout out locations with good proximity, safety, northward views and amenities to suit their needs. But you never know. You might catch your next Aurora on a road trip!

While Northern Lights do sometimes appear at the 45th Parallel and farther south, they are very rare at this latitude. In this region, it's not possible to simply go out on any given night to view the phenomenon.

If you want to catch the Northern Lights here, you either have to be really lucky, use live sightings to know when to see Aurora in the moment, or study as much as you can to understand how and when Aurora occurs.

Other factors to consider

There are other factors that may increase your chances of spotting the Northern Lights, even at low latitudes or on unlikely nights.

As you scout out the perfect viewing location for you, look for these attributes:
- High altitude will allow you to see the view low on the northern horizon more easily.
- Open views of the northern sky, cleared of tall trees or other obstacles may give you the best vantage point.
- The south side of north-facing lakes make fantastic viewing locations, because of the panoramic skies. These lakes may also give you a view of Aurora reflecting on the water or ice.
- Views to the northeast may work better early in the night, while views to the northwest may work better in the pre-dawn hours, because of the way the Aurora rises and sets.
- As always, the farther north the better!

RESOURCE > *A great way to start chasing the Aurora in safe locations is to use roadside parks or dark sky parks, which may be open 24 hours a day. Get ideas from a curated list on my website. For dark sky parks in the region, visit: KaelinArt.com/45thParallel*

Think Twice: Light Pollution, Moon Rise & That Mysterious Glow in the Distance

Passing ships in the night. Brilliant highway signs. Advertising spotlights. The glow of a purple greenhouse. A city in the distance.

As a newcomer to Aurora Chasing, it's easy to mistake many different types of light for the Aurora Borealis. Just because a light dances low on the horizon or it is green does not mean it's the Northern Lights.

Sometimes, a test shot taken on a phone or a camera will even appear green if you change your settings or turn up the saturation in photo editing. Sadly, this is not a good sign that you've caught the Aurora. Instead, you may have captured light pollution, moonlight, party lights from a faraway lakehouse, or any number of other light sources.

On camera especially, the colors of the Northern Lights should reveal themselves easily. Don't be distracted by other types of light that linger in the sky without movement or energy, or zip across the night like planned commercial gimmicks. You'll know that these artificial lights are way different then the light of the Aurora, once you get a sense of what to look for.

I always tell first-time Aurora Chasers to look for that natural quality in the Northern Lights. The colors may appear subtle or they may appear practically neon, depending on the strength of that particular display. There is a certain ethereal quality and a special brilliance to the colors of the Northern Lights.

Once you see the quintessential green of the Auroral Oval, you'll understand just how unique it truly is.

If you are instead seeing a stale, putrid yellow glow, reminiscent of a 1960's couch fabric, what you are seeing is probably light pollution. You can turn up the saturation on a light pollution photo and get this color to turn green, but that's not what you want. Instead, you want to catch the real thing!

A few tips can help you recognize light pollution:
- It doesn't really move.
- Obviously, light pollution will hover above major cities, towns or brightly lit streets, which can be identified on any map.
- The colors will appear bleak and unnatural with no vibrance.
- Light pollution radiates from the artificial lights of our streets and cities, so it will shine from the ground up and touch the bottom of the clouds. The Aurora occurs at an extremely high altitude, dancing above the clouds.

These large swaths of light can be seen from extremely far distances. It might amaze you how far light pollution can reach. You can travel 30, 60 or 90 miles away from a major light pollution center and still capture it on camera — and even farther than that. When an area of light pollution is located to the north of your location, this will become even more frustrating, because it may blot out the appearance of any Northern Lights.

For a better viewing experience, try to find a spot that does not have any major cities located to the north. Even if these cities appear to the northeast or northwest on the map, you will be in a better position to catch a northern view of the Aurora.

As you can see, there are many different sources of light that may lead you astray. These daily occurrences, along with some rare oddities, may stump you numerous times if you don't take time to learn your surroundings.

Of course, there is always that one mysterious glow in the distance. Even the most experienced Aurora Chasers can get stumped by artificial light or other atmospheric phenomena, in the right conditions. So, it never hurts to devote some time to understanding the environment you have chosen to chase the Northern Lights. That way, you'll have a better understanding of what exactly you are seeing.

RESOURCE > *Take a look at a widely used interactive dark sky map, where you can zoom in on any location in the world and view the surrounding light pollution. Because light pollution is usually caused by large cities and population centers, it remains stagnant. You can use these maps to find dark skies near you.*
For the link, visit: KaelinArt.com/45thParallel

Make or Break Your Shot: The Beauty of Night Sky Etiquette

Does it ever feel like you're on a movie set? When you go out into the darkness to admire the night sky and photograph its wonders, do the hours feel mysterious, exhilarating or unique?

You've set up your tripod. You've carefully mastered your camera settings, getting the manual focus on point. You've got your fingertip on the remote, ready to catch whatever crosses the galaxy. Maybe you've even posed a subject carefully to capture a silhouette. Then the International Space Station passes, a fireball races across the Milky Way, and a brief Aurora darts above you with vivid color and form.

You click the button. Unbelievable! Is it possible you caught it all in one frame?!

At that very moment, a bright flashlight blinds you and your camera, shining directly at your face at eye level. You look around, wondering about the source of this startling light, and find out it's not a flashlight at all. It's the tail headlights of an arriving truck. Your single frame is ruined. A surreal combination of night spectacles now appears on the back of the camera as one, huge blur of white artificial light.

Inserting artificial light into a night of photography will make or break the shot. Not only will it feel violating to the person who has been blinded by a flashlight, headlight or even a bright cell phone, but it will also overexpose any images on the camera. Some people may not care what affect this has on fellow sky watchers, but karma is real.

Someday, it could happen to you.

Why not be part of the solution? Take a few easy steps to ensure that everyone around you can enjoy the night sky, whether you know they are present or not. The beauty of night sky etiquette is that it will help you more fully embrace the night, it will add quality to your own photos, and it might even help you see things in the dark that you never realized were there.

Easy steps for Night Sky Etiquette

Are you afraid of the dark? Now is the time to overcome your fear!

Dark skies are a rapidly disappearing resource, as more people install streetlamps and other artificial lights anywhere they can. But astrophotographers and Aurora Chasers benefit from darkness. In fact, the darker the skies, the better. Only in the darkest skies will you see the most vivid colors of the Northern Lights!

When you adventure out into the night, it's important to enjoy the darkness the right way — with respect for dark skies, the land, the wildlife, and other people you may encounter.

- **Treat everyone with respect.**
  Above all, treat others with the same respect you would give to a close friend or family member during the day. The people you meet while enjoying the night sky may become mentors, supporters, or some of your closest friends.

- **Be polite and don't make assumptions.**
  Spending time in the dark brings out many different emotions for different people. You never know what a person may be thinking or experiencing when you encounter them in the dark. Give everyone the benefit of the doubt.

- **When driving to a spot, prepare to dim your vehicle lights.**
  Learn what it takes to make your vehicle as dark as possible, from the exterior to the interior lights. Turn off the headlights when you enter a parking lot, as long as it is safe to do so, and know how to dim or shut down the interior lights in case you need to be inside the car. Keep in mind that turning your car off may not be enough, because it could be programmed to keep the lights on.

- **As you arrive, point your headlights the other way.**
  Park your vehicle with the headlights facing away from the main attraction and other photographers. If you think you'll use your headlights or turn on your interior lights to check messages or warm up inside, consider parking farther away.

- **Use a blue light or a headlamp with a red light option.**
  You can find blue or red lights and other night options that are less disruptive in the dark. When you use a dimmer light, it will be gentle on your own eyes, the eyes of those around you, and wildlife that may be resting nearby. On your phone, you can also get an app or adjust the settings to make the screen dark, set it to night mode, or give it a red filter. These tools will help you maintain your night vision throughout the night.

- **Switch off any lights when you are not using them.**
  Avoid blinding others or ruining a photographer's image. Point lights straight at the ground whenever possible, and avoid turning on lights in the middle of a photography shoot. If you are in the company of other photographers, ask them when it is okay to turn on a light. They will appreciate the gesture. Night sky photographers use long exposures to capture more light on camera, meaning their shutter may stay open for long intervals, and it may still be open when you point a light in that direction.

- **Try to avoid using cellphones, devices, or other screens beside night sky photographers.**
  If you want to check your device, you can take 5-10 steps backward and away from the camera to minimize ambient light.

- **Never walk in front of a camera.**
  Aurora photographers use a number of devices to get the best photos at night, including automated time-lapses and remotes. A camera may be busy working even if it looks like no one is using it. Always walk behind the tripod, instead of in front of it. If you see a large set-up of camera gear, take the extra time and walk around it, instead of following the straightest path.

- **Consider others before you add sources of light to a scene.**
  Often, it's tempting to build bonfires or to bring other types of

light into dark spaces. However, sometimes even having a fire can obscure the visibility of the Northern Lights. If you want to build a fire or hold other activities, discuss it with those around you, and move far away from the photographers first, so you can set up somewhere behind them. If you do use artificial light purposefully or as a prop in your photos, be considerate of others as you decide where to place the light.

- **Leave no trace.**
  As lovers of natural beauty, it's up to us to protect the public land and resources available to us, so that it will still be there and remain accessible in future years. If you carry any items with you, make sure you carry out all the same items, including any trash you've created. Leave no trace that you've been there.

- **Enjoy a friendly and welcoming atmosphere.**
  Remember, many night sky enthusiasts may be experiencing the night for the first time. Share your enthusiasm, knowledge and support!

Everyone has different preferences when they wander out in the dark of the night. Keep in mind that some people prefer to be alone, some prefer to spend time in large groups, and some people may even be seeking quiet.

Did you know that you can sometimes hear the Northern Lights? It's true! But only if you listen closely. Research has shown that it's possible to hear the sound of the Aurora, although this is a controversial belief in some circles. I've never experienced this myself, but from what I understand, the sound can be detected during the strongest geomagnetic storms. If listening for the Aurora is something you want to try, you may want to prioritize a quiet viewing location, one that is remote and far from the commotion of towns, cities or popular camp sites.

On the flip side, some people may quickly find themselves in over their heads if they leave the house unprepared. Anything from bitter cold, punishing wind, broken gear, personal injury, or flat tires can threaten to ruin a night under the stars.

Don't forget to prepare well for a journey chasing the Northern Lights. Plan this trip out and pack well for it, like you would for any other trip where you might take a faraway vacation or venture into the wilderness. Remember that the more remote your location, the more unlikely it is that you will have cell phone service when you get there.

Calling for help may be more difficult on a night of chasing the Aurora, sheerly because of your location. It never hurts to tell someone about your trip and notify them of when you plan to return, in case something goes wrong and you can't be reached.

You can also learn about the ten essentials to pack on every trip, and keep safety items and reserves in your car, such as bottles of water. Be patient, give each person the benefit of the doubt, and honor individual preferences. A little kindness goes a long way.

A fantastic community of Aurora Chasers enjoys these adventures in the Great Lakes region, and we hope the tradition of chasing the Northern Lights in the mid-latitudes can continue to inspire people for many years to come. Thank you for making the Aurora Chasing community safe, friendly and welcoming!

RESOURCE > *Discover what it could be like to hear the Aurora, when you listen to a recording that's been vetted by scientists. To listen to this audio, visit: KaelinArt.com/45thParallel*

BONUS: Beginning Photography Tips from the Unphotographer

One of the things that surprises people most about me is that I am not an Aurora photographer. At least, I don't consider myself one, although on rare occasions I have taken gorgeous photos of the Northern Lights. Instead, I am drawn to the experience of watching the Northern Lights dance with my own eyes, to enjoy one of nature's rare natural phenomenon in all her glory!

I find the act of viewing the Aurora Borealis with the unaided eye invigorating and amazing. The mystery, wonder and unmistakable electric sensation of each display inspires my creativity and my writing long after the brilliant colors, movement, and light subside.

Sure, I've taken test shots of the sky on quiet nights to try to detect the presence of the Aurora from the mid-latitudes before it becomes visible to the naked eye. But I usually do this using my cell phone camera. Also, it wasn't until the release of newer mobile phones like the iPhone 14 that I was able to capture a crystal clear photo of the Aurora Borealis at night, with minimal effort, glorious moonlit foregrounds and nearly perfect pinpoint stars in the composition.

Phone cameras have come a long way, especially since 2020! So, it might be time for you to cash in that upgrade, and experiment with taking night sky photographs on your own device.

That's not to say DSLR photography is going out of style. I personally believe phones will never replace the sheer beauty and expert nightscapes that can be captured using the advanced cameras, lenses, accessories, remotes and other technology that abound in the photography world. If you are seriously interested in pursuing Aurora photography, I highly recommend picking up a DSLR camera.

Over the years, I've spent a lot of time with photographers, recruiting speakers to offer workshops to beginners and watching these artists as they capture the Northern Lights in the night sky. While I am not a seasoned Aurora photographer, I can give you some essential advice that will make a world of difference for you when you are starting out. These tips will take you far in your journey to create stunning night sky images.

1. Take a test shot.
As you now know, the Northern Lights are not always visible to the unaided eye. Use any camera or device on manual settings and take a test shot any time you think Aurora may be present. You may be surprised to see that the camera registers vivid color, even when your eyes see nothing.

2. Always use a tripod.
As the Aurora dances across the sky, capturing a photo that is not blurry, grainy or ruined with noise becomes one of the biggest challenges. A tripod is a game changer. Make sure you bring a tripod any time you want to photograph the Northern Lights, even if you are hoping to photograph them using your cell phone. The tripod will ensure that you can take clear, focused photographs, and in the case of cell phones, it may be the ticket to activating your long exposure settings.

3. Skip the telescope, go manual, and get a wider lens.
A telescope won't help you see the Northern Lights, because it will narrow your view and focus on pinpoint areas of the night sky. Instead, you'll want to have as broad a view as possible. Ideally, the Aurora will become so strong that they will leap overhead — and the lights might even dance above or behind you.

Skip the automatic functions on your camera and go manual. Learn to use your camera in manual mode, adjusting your aperture and shutter speed to the ideal settings for that particular display. The settings you use may vary with each show, just as the brightness, color, and speed of the Aurora will vary.

If you're lucky enough to catch a geomagnetic storm or view an all-sky display, you'll want a wide camera lens. Some displays may only be visible low on the horizon, but other displays will give you an opportunity to capture Aurora directly overhead or to catch the famous STEVE, as the sub-auroral arc stretches from one horizon to the other.

4. Never try to learn your equipment on the chase.
The biggest mistake many new photographers make is to buy a camera hours before they photograph an Aurora, without ever having used the camera in daylight. This happens with tripods, too. Believe it or not, it's really difficult to learn new camera gear in the dark!

Do yourself a favor and practice setting up your tripod and camera before the big night. Experiment with your settings and lenses. Test out your remote. Pack extra batteries in case your batteries run out of juice in the middle of the display. The more prepared you are for a Northern Lights display, the more relaxing the experience will be.

5. Now's your time! Focus on a star.
One of the most difficult obstacles for beginning astrophotographers is focusing in the dark. After your camera is secured on the tripod, placed in the right position, and set to manual, start the night by focusing on a star. This will help you keep your camera in focus, even as the dynamic Northern Lights begin their lively and unpredictable dance.

RESOURCE > *Find articles and video tutorials that will help you learn what you need to know to get started in Aurora photography. For links to these online resources, visit: KaelinArt.com/45thParallel*

Sneak Peek!

Enjoy an excerpt of my fiction, which will be released in a short story collection in the coming year. The excerpt features a scene at the Lake of the Clouds in the Porcupine Mountains, which is located in Michigan's beautiful Upper Peninsula. The storytelling is also part of a project to garner representation for my first novel, which has a working title of "Whistle on Whiteface Mountain." The novel manuscript is under consideration by a major talent agency.

To receive news, updates and book announcements, please subscribe to my newsletter at: KaelinArt.com/subscribe

The Wrong Latitude

WEDNESDAY, JULY 17, 2013

Cold air, light clouds and a galaxy of stars greeted Clarence, who stood high above the lake in the Porcupine Mountains. Overtop of his charcoal beanie, he wore a headlamp with the white light switched on. He planted his feet firmly on the basalt rock cliff, and set up a tripod under the moonless night.

"Steady as she goes," Clarence called down the rocks.

Another tripod made its way up the cliff, this one held high in the air by the young man behind it. He was decked out in athletic apparel, and he wore a multicolor knit-hat streaming with braided tassels. The young man smiled broadly, revealing teeth so white they were visible in the dark. If it weren't for his wildly colorful clothing, he would've blended in to the night with his short, black hair and copper-toned skin.

"Tyler, lad, why don't you set that down until you get the lay of the land?" Clarence asked. "Turn on your headlamp."

"I got it," Tyler said, without an ounce of hesitation. He wore a headlamp too, but it was switched off. He wasn't even using the dim red light designed to navigate the dark. Tyler fumbled over the uneven ledge, dipping the tripod toward the ground, before he found his footing on the rocks. He stood about 30 feet away from Clarence, occupying slightly higher ground.

The two men had spread out on a long, narrow escarpment, attempting to set up a photo overlooking the Lake of the Clouds. A Coronal Mass Ejection, which had fired from the surface of the sun a few days ago, was predicted to make impact tonight. If it was powerful enough, the Earth's atmosphere would open up to the solar wind, funneling in a wave of electrons and producing a vivid display of Northern Lights.

"Move the tripod to the left," Clarence said. "Let's capture a silhouette against the night."

"Of me?" Tyler laughed. He picked up the tripod, scanning the rocks for another flat surface. "It was your idea to come up here. I didn't even know there was a mountain range in Michigan. You guys call these mountains?"

"You've been spending too much time in Canada," Clarence said, teasing him. "Not much compares to Banff National Park."

"You said it!" Tyler was studying the northern horizon. "Sure is easier to catch a glimpse in Alberta."

"No doubt that it is."

"When was the last time I saw you on the Aurora Chasing trail?"

"A year ago? Maybe two?" Tyler pondered the question. "Seems like it's been quite a while."

It was quiet and still all around them. Set against a pristine wilderness, the Porcupine Mountains were wound through with streams and old-growth Hemlock forests. Clarence reveled in the quiet energy of the forest at night. Even when their voices were muted, he and Tyler could hear each other loud and clear.

"Get in the frame," Clarence urged. His camera was set up on the tripod and ready to fire.

"Are you getting something?"

"The faintest hint of green. Now, lad, this is going to take some time. I need you to choose a position, and hold very, very still."

"For how long?"

Clarence didn't answer. Instead, he adjusted the settings on his camera, capturing as much light from the sky as possible while still keeping the guy in focus. "Now, don't move."

"Like this?" Tyler, ever the star of his own antics, had struck a pose that required some skillful balance. He balled his hands into fists and held them out in the air, while he lifted one leg and bent his knee, to create what might look like an action shot.

"No talking."

"You serious?" Tyler cocked his head.

It was all for fun, but getting a crisp night shot took planning and commitment. Tyler balked at being frozen in time, eager to set up his own astrophotography shots. He lost his balance, and tilted toward his last leg standing, dropping out of position and jogging a few feet to catch himself.

The shutter on Clarence's camera clicked.

"Well, lad, that'll be interesting."

Tyler laughed. "I couldn't hold it!"

"Might be wise to start with both feet on the ground next time," Clarence said good-naturedly. He moved his camera into preview mode, and he mused at the digital image. With his index finger, he traced the falling action he'd watched in real time, and observed how Tyler's body took form in the photo. A thin, white layer of color moved from where the silhouette once stood, and nearly wiped out on the rocks, before disappearing on the left side of the frame. "There's a ghost in this shot."

"Maybe it's the Aurora," Tyler countered.

"Wrong altitude."

"You know, this isn't exactly the easiest latitude for chasing either!"

"It all depends upon your perspective."

"Right on. Ok, I'm going to set up some star trails."

"Alright." Clarence chuckled. "Go on then."

In his seventies, Clarence was a spry old man. He hadn't thought twice about scaling the escarpment in the dark and shooting star trails and Aurora with a guy in his twenties. That was the easy part. It was the standing still, waiting for the camera to work its magic and capture the night sky, that was the hard part. Especially on cold nights like this one.

A cold snap had blown in from Canada, and the temperature in northern Michigan plummeted to a mere 38 degrees. Factor in the breeze, and it was finger freezing weather. Always prepared for the unexpected, Clarence reached into his coat pockets and fetched a set of thick gloves. He slid the gloves over his wide, wrinkled fingers, and sat down on a fallen log by the hemlocks. He reached into his pocket once more, and pulled out a single film photograph.

The photo was folded to fit in his pocket, but he bent back the edge and gazed into its face.

Warm green eyes stared back out at Clarence, softened even more by a broad, cheerful smile. The girl's auburn hair was pulled back in a tight ponytail, and she hugged her arms close around her body, bundled up in a thick blue coat. Behind her, snow blanketed a frozen lake, and beyond her, the Aurora Borealis glowed green to match her teardrop eyes.

"Laura," he whispered.

His daughter had been lovely and bright, and she had grown to a tender age of 10 before she died from a brain tumor. He looked up from the photo, and saw Tyler come strolling back across the rocks.

"It's in the bag," Tyler said. "I've got it set to shoot one frame every five minutes. That should do the trick." He plopped down beside Clarence, saw the photograph, and lowered his voice to a whisper. "Who's the girl?"

"The light of my life," Clarence said. "My only child."

"Where is she now?"

"Following the torches, I suppose," he said. "To paradise."

"Torches?"

"It's an ancient Inuit myth." Clarence combed his fingers through his silver beard. "The indigenous tribes of the North believed the Aurora Borealis were torches. The flames were lit by their ancestors, who carried the torches through the sky, leading their loved ones to paradise."

Tyler studied the old man's face.

"Just some old folklore," Clarence said.

"I'm sorry," Tyler said. "How long has it been?"

"Forty-two years."

"Is that why you live alone?"

Clarence had to stop to consider the question. Surrounded by a thriving natural wilderness, he didn't think of himself as a loner. He was, of course. Until he found an excuse to meet up with his nocturnal companions – sky-watchers, star-gazers, storm-chasers.

"You do live alone, right?"

"Well, sure," Clarence said. "But it wasn't always this way. Laura's passing was quite unexpected. It was too much for Veronica to bear."

"Your wife?"

Clarence nodded. "She used to be. She left me and moved to another state, to leave all this behind."

"Why did she leave?"

"Well, lad, I can't answer that. The truth is I don't know." Clarence bent back the edge of the photograph again, and gazed at his long lost daughter. "I guess it was something she had to do. But when she moved away, it left me alone in our house in Grand Rapids. So, I sold the place and moved north."

Tyler stood up. "North is a solid choice," he declared. He looked down at his elderly friend, who was still gazing into the photograph, and gave him a firm pat on the back. Then he turned toward the cameras, and went to check on his star trails.

Clarence glanced up, if only for a second. He ran his gloved fingers over the glossy photograph, tracing the shape of his daughter's hair, her nose, and her crooked smile. At eight years old, the girl in the photo had seen the Aurora that night, staying up late to go with her father to his favorite lake in northern Michigan.

Tears ran down Clarence's face in large, slow drops. He looked at the black sky above the Lake of the Clouds, tracing the Milky Way with his eyes. The galaxy was brilliant tonight, appearing in shades of purple and burnt sienna. Millions of stars stretched out above him, winking and comforting him with their light. But the sky carried no torches. It showed no signs of Lady Aurora.

When the tears dried, Clarence felt alone. Tyler was just over the rocks, setting up a second camera. But this wasn't a simple loneliness that could be solved with just any companionship.

Once a transcendent experience, the Aurora had become an obsession. It still brought him joy and inner calm, but now he needed it to fill the empty space in his heart.

Like the ancient Inuit tribes, he would watch the mysterious lights move above him and contemplate the spirit world. Every once in a while, he envisioned his daughter up there, the daisies on her green dress dashing through the sky.

Unwavering in their chase of the Northern Lights, the two men waited. Clarence would give anything for a hint of that peaceful fever. The solar wind fascinated him more than anything on Earth. The celestial phenomenon moved him to his core.

Though they stayed out all night, it was no use.

The marvels of outer space wouldn't be visible tonight.

.   .   .

To read more stories, poetry and novels,
visit: KaelinArt.com/writing

About the Author

An avid adventurer, Melissa F. Kaelin discovered her passion for the Northern Lights when she was living in Minnesota, just south of Minneapolis and St. Paul. The morning after April 24, 2012, she awoke to a brilliant display of photographs posted across local and national news outlets. She was born and raised in Ohio, and

it wasn't until she reached her late twenties that she realized the Northern Lights could be seen in their full glory, right here in the lower 48 states of the continental U.S.

On that day, Melissa decided she would do whatever it took to view the Aurora Borealis with her own eyes, even at low latitudes. She began studying space weather and aurora forecasting and joined social media groups to learn as much as she could about this rare natural phenomenon. Because her residence was situated in a light pollution desert below the 45th Parallel, she found it extremely difficult to catch the Aurora's dance for the first time.

She continued to study space weather, hoping to understand the conditions that could reliably create a geomagnetic storm strong enough to detect with the unaided eye. After several failed attempts, Melissa witnessed her first display of the Northern Lights on the night of Oct. 1, 2013 in Taylors Falls, Minnesota.

She also discovered that the mythology and legends of the Inuit tribes of North America closely matched her own perception of the Aurora Borealis, which have become an almost spiritual experience in her life. So, she began to research stories of the Aurora and learn Aurora legends from cultures around the world. She has spoken as a conference presenter on Aurora forecasting for beginners and on Aurora Mythology and Legend.

Melissa has followed her passion for the Aurora, rare natural phenomena, and the wonders of the night sky to soaring heights. She partnered with two devoted Aurora Chasers, Dr. Mike Shaw and Dixie J. Burbank, to launch the Aurora Summit, an annual celebration of the Northern Lights that opened to the public in 2017. The unique event draws up to 200 people each year, and it includes sessions on the science, art, photography and culture that surround the Northern Lights.

Fascinated with outer space, Melissa went on to serve as a NASA Social Media Ambassador for the launch of the ESA Solar Orbiter at Cape Canaveral in February 2020. She has published many articles, short stories, and features that center around the night sky, as well as the legends and mythology that have been passed down for centuries. She wrote a novel manuscript featuring the mythology of the Aurora Borealis, which is under consideration in the publishing industry, and she is working on two other novel concepts featuring the Solar Eclipse and the Milky Way.

Melissa has also stepped up to serve as an admin for several social media groups devoted to the Northern Lights and the night sky. In January 2021, she founded the Michigan Aurora Chasers, which grew to 58,000 members and climbing in the first two years since its inception.

Like many in the community, Melissa finds inspiration in sharing the Aurora's enchanting dance with others. While she does not typically photograph the rare phenomenon with a D-SLR camera, Aurora inspires many aspects of her life, particularly in creative writing. She hopes to help more people find, understand, and celebrate the elusive Northern Lights — which continue to be a rare spectacle at low latitudes.

More details about her life and creative work can be found on the website: KaelinArt.com/aurora-chaser

Follow on social media:
Instagram.com/mfkaelin
Twitter.com/mfkaelin
Facebook.com/KaelinArt

Become Part of the Adventure!

Browse my blog on Aurora Chasing in the U.S.:
KaelinArt.com/aurora-blog

Attend the annual Aurora Summit:
TheAuroraSummit.com

Join the Michigan Aurora Chasers:
Facebook.com/groups/MichiganAuroraChasers

Digital Resource Guide

Get more out of this guidebook using the digital companion. The Digital Resource Guide includes details on every resource mentioned in the book, as well as other links.

View the Online Resource Guide:
KaelinArt.com/45thParallel

---

*Good luck on the
Aurora Chasing trail!*

*— Melissa F. Kaelin
Writer, Artist & Stargazer
KaelinArt.com*

13701212R00037